The Best
Manchester City
Trivia Book Ever

300+ Interesting Trivia Questions and Random,
Shocking, Fun Facts Every Cityzen Needs to Know

Contents

YOUR FREE BONUS!

The 11 Most Iconic Moments in Football History

In this special edition, you'll discover the secret stories behind them.

Enjoy!

Find out by scanning the QR Code below with your smartphone:

INTRODUCTION

Manchester is an important City in European football.

It is the birthplace and seat of one of the fiercest rivalries in football. The Red Devils of Manchester United do battle with their *noisy neighbors*, the Citizens (Cityzens) of Manchester City, who have been more successful in recent years.

But the truth is, "It is the Manchester City era!!!"

And every other English club is just living in the shadow of the Cityzens!

Four titles in five seasons in blistering, totally-dominant fashion and shouts of "the Best Premier League side ever" fill the headlines daily to remind football fans of who is the current best English side by a country mile. The tenacity of Carlos Tevez, Vincent Kompany and Joleon Lescott has given way to the frightening potential of Phil Foden, the surgical creativity of De Bruyne and the excellence of Rodri. Silva to Jesus has paved the way for Silva to Haaland. And the success has not stopped. Nobody knows how to stop this City side!!!

It was not always this rosy for Manchester City and Sir Alex Ferguson of Manchester United who famously referred to City as the *noisy neighbors*. These days, the noise at Etihad Stadium is of joy and excitement by exuberant fans entertained by perhaps the best side the league has ever seen.

Manchester City was founded by members of St Mark's Church of England as a way to reduce local gang violence and alcoholism in the unemployment-high Gorton area of East Manchester. It was supposed to be a substitute for the cricket club during winter and was named St Mark's appropriately. The club then won the FA cup in 1904 to become the first team from Manchester to win a major title, a fact that rankles deeply within Manchester United ranks.

The 1960s and 1970s were a period of dominance for Manchester City Football Club. The Cityzens won a league title, the FA Cup, the League Cup and the European Cup Winners' Cup. Unfortunately, this was followed by a lean period topped ultimately with relegation from the Premier League in 1996. The club floundered in the lower leagues until 2001/02 when they regained elite status.

More good news was on the way, though. A new stadium was completed in 2003 and a few years later , the *noisy neighbors* became the *rich neighbors*. In 2008 the Abu Dhabi United Group, which was directed by Sheikh Mansour bin Zayed Al Nahyan, completed a takeover of City and changed the English Football landscape forever. Big names like Robinho, Gareth Barry, the Toure brothers, Emmanuel Adebayor, Joleon Lescott, and Carlos Tevez sauntered through the door to transform City.

Considerable investment and the appointment of top coaches has seen Manchester City become the team to beat in England. An FA cup triumph in 2011 and the Premier League title a year after heralded a new dawn. That dawn has since lived up to its billing.

On February 1st 2016, City announced that they had managed to secure the services of Pep Guardiola, acclaimed by many as the best coach on the planet. In the seven seasons he has since spent, there is little evidence to the contrary. Four titles in the last five seasons tell only half of the story of dominance that his possession-based team has created. The 100 points they secured in 2017/18 was unprecedented in English football history. They followed this with another league title in the next season.

With the rise of Manchester City, Manchester United can no longer claim exclusive rights over amazing comebacks and the most dramatic moments in the Premier League. Instead, the *Aguerooooo* moment in 2012/13 stands as evidence of the spirit of the Cityzens.

In the 2021/22 season, another dramatic comeback handed City the title. With two games left and needing at least a win and a draw to win the league, City fell behind by two goals to West Ham in the penultimate game and had to battle to a 2-2 draw. In the season finale, City conceded two goals to Aston Villa and were staring down the barrel. Luckily, you can never say "die" with this club. Three goals duly arrived in 5 minutes after the 76th minute.

An interesting footnote to the current era is the rivalry with Liverpool. Liverpool can certainly feel hard-done by City after losing two league titles to the Cityzens by a single point. Jurgen Klopp of Liverpool and Pep Guardiola were also former derby rivals in the German Der Klassiker while the former was at Borussia Dortmund and the latter was at Bayern Munich. The rivalry sometimes threatens to boil over and adds a layer of spectacle to their matches.

The stats do not lie about Manchester City – they are absolute giants of the game. In terms of trophies collected, City is the fifth most successful club in English football. City has played in the UCL for twelve consecutive seasons and qualified for the knockouts for ten successive seasons. As if that is not enough, they also have huge marketing pull and in 2021, they topped the Deloitte Football Money League with revenues of 644 million euros.

A goalkeeper with a broken neck; the famous "Why Always Me" celebration; Aguerrrrooooo; the unbelievable 6-1 drubbing of Sir Alex Ferguson's Red Devils; Kompany hitting a worldie into the Leicester goal; Yaya Toure majestically strolling through the opponents' midfield; Gundogan rolling the ball into the net for the title; Jesus' lob to secure 100 points and Guardiola sprinting down the touchline are just some of the iconic moments that City fans have been treated to.

And with the signing of the giant, monstrous Nordic striker, Erling Haaland, son of former City star, Alfie Haaland, the merry train does not appear to be slowing down.

It is hard to keep up with the rich history and current achievements of Manchester City, and this is where this trivia book comes in handy.

With twelve chapters filled with a wide range of questions, and 10 fun-filled trivia facts each, you are introduced to the story of Manchester City in a way you have not seen before. We cover everything from Hyde Road through Maine Road and the unprecedented era at the Etihad stadium.

Manchester City has been here forever and now that they are in the driving seat, the sky seems to be the starting point. Join us on this exciting exploration of the culture, history, and prospects of Manchester City. The swashbuckling, possession-heavy, dominant football style inspired by Pep is only one facet of the existence of this modern club.

Do you want to win the next City trivia quiz you participate in?

Do you need fun facts for an evening out with family members?

Do you want to know more about Manchester City, its players, legends and coaches?

Are you a casual football fan trying to take a peek into the groundwork for the current dominance?

Then, you are in luck!!!

Sit back and dive into Manchester City's world as you have never seen it before!!!

ORIGIN

"At the time, West Gorton was an area of tremendous deprivation. There was overcrowding, squalor, poor sanitation, and poverty, and the ways in which the men of the community sought refuge from this was drink and gang warfare, which was called 'scuttling' in that era"

– Peter Lupson

20 Trivia Questions

1. The club that came to be known as Manchester City Football Club was founded in the year _____?

    A. 1880

    B. 1879

    C. 1881

    D. 1890

2. At inception, Manchester City was known by which of these names?

    A. Union Iron Works

    B. St Marks

    C. South Gorton

    D. East Gorton

3. The club was founded at the behest of _____?

    A. Thomas Goodbehere

    B. William Beastow

    C. The Connells, Arthur and Anna

    D. St Mark's Church

4. The church wardens that formed St Mark's church team held senior positions at
    _____?

    A. City Council

    B. Sheriff's Department

    C. First Aid Society

    D. Union Iron Works

5. What was another common name for St Mark's church team?

    A. East Gorton

    B. West Gorton

    C. South Gorton

    D. North Gorton

6. St Mark's first recorded match was played against another church team. Where
    were the opponents from?

    A. Macclesfield

    B. Mansfield

    C. Luton

    D. Crewe

7. How many matches were won by St Mark's in the club's first season?

    A. 2

    B. 0

    C. 1

    D. 5

8. What were the first kit colors of St Mark's team?

    A. Sky-blue

    B. Yellow

    C. Green

    D. Black

9. When did St Mark evolve into Ardwick AFC?

    A. 1883

    B. 1885

    C. 1887

    D. 1889

10. When did Ardwick AFC move into the ground on Hyde Road?

    A. 1886

    B. 1887

    C. 1889

    D. 1888

11. When was the Football League Second Division created?

    A. 1892

    B. 1878

    C. 1906

    D. 1915

12. Ardwick AFC joined the Football League Second Division in the year _____?

    A. 1920

    B. 1910

    C. 1900

    D. 1892

13. Ardwick AFC reformed into Manchester City in an attempt to _____?

    A. Attract sponsorship

    B. Sound catchy

    C. Represent the whole city

    D. Become famous

14. The current traditional Manchester City colours of sky-blue were adopted in _____?

    A. 1888

    B. 1894

    C. 1904

    D. 1926

15. Manchester City's first ever title win came in the _____?

    A. Second Division

    B. Lancashire Division

    C. FA Cup

    D. First Division

16. How many English Football League teams had won automatic promotion before Manchester City?

    A. 3

    B. 2

    C. 1

    D. 0

17. The 1904 FA Cup Final won by Manchester City was held at _____?

    A. Manchester

    B. Lancashire

    C. Crystal Palace

    D. Tottenham

18. Which team contested and lost the 1904 FA Cup final against Manchester City?

    A. Wolverhampton Wanderers

    B. Bolton Wanderers

    C. Charlton

    D. Everton

19. In which season did Manchester City play in the First Division for the first time?

    A.   1899/1900

    B.   1889/1890

    C.   1888/1889

    D.   1906/1907

20. How many City players were suspended in the year 1904?

    A.   6

    B.   10

    C.   12

    D.   17

20 Trivia Answers

1. A – 1880

2. B – St Mark's

3. C – The Connells, Arthur and Anna

4. D – Union Iron Works

5. B – West Gorton

6. A – Macclesfield

7. C – 1

8. D – Black

9. C – 1887

10. B – 1887

11. A – 1892

12. D – 1892

13. C – Represent the whole city

14. B – 1894

15. A – Second Division

16. D – 0

17. C – Crystal Palace

18. B – Bolton Wanderers

19. A – 1899/1900

20. D – 17

10 Fun Facts

1. The football club today known as Manchester City was founded by members of St Mark's church of England in 1880 as a form of humanitarian gesture to the people of West Gorton, a place that was plagued by unemployment and crime at the time. The Church had founded a Cricket Club in 1875 but still saw a need for another endeavor to keep locals occupied during the winter months.

2. William Beastow and Thomas Goodbehere, church wardens at St Marks and holders of senior roles at the Union Iron Works, formed a church team known as St marks (West Gorton) in the winter of 1880 at the behest of Arthur Connell, the then Rector of St Mark's church and his daughter Anna Connell, who sought to curb social vices plaguing the area at the time.

3. St Mark's first recorded match was played against another church team from Macclesfield in November 1880. St Marks lost 2-1. Their only win in their first season was against Stalybridge Clarence in March 1881.

4. The first colours used by the club were black with a Maltese-style cross. Some refer this choice of colour to the club's cordial links with Freemasonry in the 1880s while others believe the white cross showed the connection to St Mark's Church was still strong at the time. The occasional use of black and red away kits is in keeping with former City assistant manager Malcom Allison's belief that adopting the colours of Italian Serie A side AC Milan would inspire City to success.

5. St Mark's church team evolved into Ardwick Association Football Club (AFC) in 1887 and moved to a new ground on Hyde Road around the same period.

6. Ardwick AFC were elected into the English Football League in 1892, when the Second Division was created with Ardwick as one of its founding members.

7. In an attempt to represent the whole city of Manchester, Ardwick AFC were reformed into Manchester City Football Club in 1894. The present-day traditional home colour of sky-blue was also adopted around that period.

8. Manchester City finished top of the Second Division in 1899, winning their first trophy and becoming the first team to gain automatic promotion in English Football League history.

9. Manchester City beat Bolton Wanderers 1-0 in the 1904 FA Cup final held at Crystal Palace to become the first club from Manchester to win a major trophy. In the same season, City finished runner-up in the First Division.

10. A spate of financial misdemeanors resulted in the suspension of 17 Manchester City players including club captain Billy Meredith in 1904.. Meredith crossed the Manchester divide to join rivals United shortly after his suspension.

STADIUM

"We have a real bite to our game now and we will add strength in depth. Coming to the Etihad Stadium will not be easy for anyone next season."

– Roberto Mancini

20 Trivia Questions

1. At how many different grounds did City play home games before moving to Hyde Road?

    A. 5

    B. 1

    C. 3

    D. 2

2. When did Manchester City move into the ground on Hyde Road?

    A. 1885

    B. 1886

    C. 1888

    D. 1887

3. The main Stand at Hyde Road was destroyed in 1920 as a result of _____?

    A. Word War I

    B. Fire accident

    C. Flood

    D. Lighting and thunderstorms

4. Which stadium had the nickname "Wembley of the North"

    A. Hyde Road

    B. Etihad Stadium

    C. Maine Road

    D. Old Wembley

5. Hyde Road hosted a reigning monarch for the first time in the year _____?

    A. 1921

    B. 1920

    C. 1919

    D. 1922

6. At the time City moved to Hyde Road, the club was named _____?

    A. St Mark's

    B. West Gorton

    C. Manchester City

    D. Ardwick AFC

7. For how many years did Manchester City play at Hyde Road?

    A. 36 years

    B. 24 years

    C. 23 years

    D. 30 years

8. The fire accident that destroyed Hyde Road's Main Stand happened in _____?

    A. 1913

    B. 1925

    C. 1920

    D. 1924

9. City's first ever Premier League game at Maine Road was played against _____?

    A. Everton

    B. Queens Park Rangers

    C. Coventry City

    D. AFC Wimbledon

10. Which player scored City's first Premier League goal at Maine Road?

    A. Paul Lake

    B. Rick Holden

    C. David Kerr

    D. David White

11. A club record crowd attended City's game against which of these teams?

    A. Blackburn Rovers

    B. Bolton Wanderers

    C. Stoke City

    D. Millwall

12. City's biggest ever win at Maine Road was against which of these teams?

    A. Huddersfield Town

    B. Sunderland

    C. Charlton Athletic

    D. Sheffield Wednesday

13. The City of Manchester Stadium was commissioned in the year _____?

    A. 2000

    B. 2003

    C. 2001

    D. 2002

14. What is the score of City's biggest ever Manchester derby win at Maine Road?

    A. 7-1

    B. 6-1

    C. 5-1

    D. 3-1

15. City's last ever Premier League game at Maine Road was played against _____?

    A. Southampton

    B. Aston Villa

    C. Leeds United

    D. Leicester City

16. City's last Premier League goal at Maine Road was scored by _____?

    A. Robert Fowler

    B. Richard Walker

    C. Nicolas Anelka

    D. Marc-Vivien Foe

17. Which player scored City's first ever UEFA Champions League goal at the City of Manchester Stadium?

    A. Vincent Kompany

    B. Yaya Toure

    C. Edin Dzeko

    D. Aleksandar Kolarov

18. City's first Champions League game at the City of Manchester Stadium was against _____?

    A. Villareal

    B. Napoli

    C. Bayern Munich

    D. Porto

19. For how many years did City play at Maine Road?

    A. 70

    B. 75

    C. 80

    D. 85

20. City played at Maine Road for the first time in the year _____?

    A. 1932

    B. 1923

    C. 1919

    D. 1946

20 Trivia Answers

1. A – 5

2. D – 1887

3. B – Fire accident

4. C – Maine Road

5. B – 1920

6. D – Ardwick AFC

7. A – 36 years

8. C – 1920

9. B – Queens Park Rangers

10. D – David White

11. C – Stoke City

12. A – Huddersfield Town

13. B – 2003

14. C – 5-1

15. A – Southampton

16. D – Marc-Vivien Foe

17. D – Aleksandar Kolarov

18. B – Napoli

19. C – 80

20. B – 1923

10 Fun Facts

1. Manchester City (then known as Ardwick AFC) moved into a ground on Hyde Road in 1887 after playing their home games at five different grounds since the club was founded in 1880.

2. In 1920, Manchester City's Hyde Road ground became the first provincial football stadium to have the honour of hosting a reigning monarch. The main stand at the ground was destroyed in a fire accident soon afterwards.

3. Three years after the Hyde Road fire accident, Manchester City moved to a new purpose-built stadium having a capacity of 85,000 located on Maine Road in Moss Side. The stadium's designers nicknamed it "The Wembley of the North."

4. Manchester City's Maine Road ground set a record attendance of 84,569 spectators for the visit of Stoke City in an FA Cup tie in March 1934. Only Wembley Stadium has held a bigger crowd in a competitive game in English football.

5. City's Maine Road ground had undergone several redevelopments and its capacity was down to 32,000 by the year 1995. This prompted the club to begin the search for a bigger stadium.

6. City's local rivals Manchester United were forced to use Maine Road due to substantial damages to their Old Trafford ground during World War II. However, City still used the home dressing room whenever the two teams met.

7. In 1994, legislation brought an end of terracing at Premier League grounds and prompted the closure of City's beloved Kippax Stand at their Maine Road Stadium. The Kippax Stand had the largest standing area in the whole country.

8. Manchester City recorded their biggest ever win at Maine Road in a 10-1 rout of Huddersfield Town in 1987. Two years later, they recorded the biggest Manchester derby win at Maine Road, pummeling Manchester United 5-1.

9. Manchester City played their last ever game at Maine Road on 11 May 2003 against Southampton in the Premier League. The visitors won the game 1-0 thanks to Michael Svenson's first half goal.

10. After spending the last 80 years playing at Maine Road, Manchester City moved into the City of Manchester Stadium (now known as the Etihad Stadium) at the start the 2003/04 season. The new ground had an impressive capacity of 48,000.

MANAGERS

"We played the best football. We scored the most goals, we conceded the fewest. We beat United twice. In the history of the club, a final like this does not exist. I'm very proud of my players though. To win the championship like this, I think it will be impossible for the next 100 years."

– Roberto Mancini

20 Trivia Questions

1. Who was Manchester Citys' manager when they played in the UEFA Champions League for the first time?

    A. Mark Hughes

    B. Roberto Mancini

    C. Manuel Pellegrini

    D. Stuart Pearce

2. Manchester City won their maiden First Division title under which of these managers?

    A. Stuart Pearce

    B. Les McDowall

    C. Wilf Wild

    D. David Ashworth

3. Who was City manager when the club first played in the Premier League?

    A. Brian Horton

    B. Peter Reid

    C. Alan Ball

    D. Steve Coppell

4. The only City manager to guide the club to success in a European club competition is _____?

   A. Tony Brook

   B. Mark Hughes

   C. Les McDowall

   D. Joe Mercer

5. The last City manager to take charge of the club in the Europa League is _____?

   A. Mark Hughes

   B. Sven-Goran Eriksson

   C. Roberto Mancini

   D. Manuel Pellegrini

6. Who was Manchester City manager at the time football was paused due to World War I?

   A. Harry Newbould

   B. Ernest Mangnall

   C. Wilf Wild

   D. Tom Maley

7. Wilf Wild left the post of City manager in _____?

   A. 1946

   B. 1968

   C. 1970

   D. 1952

8. Which of these former City managers took charge of the club's first game in the European Cup?

    A. George Poyser

    B. Joe Mercer

    C. Malcolm Allison

    D. Ron Saunders

9. What is the nationality of former City manager, Manuel Pellegrini?

    A. Colombian

    B. Italian

    C. Brazilian

    D. Chilean

10. City suffered relegation from the Premier League for the only time under which of these managers?

    A. Alan Ball

    B. Brian Horton

    C. Roberto Mancini

    D. Frank Clark

11. The shortest period any manager has stayed at Manchester City is _____?

    A. 30 days

    B. 31 days

    C. 32 days

    D. 33 days

12. The shortest-serving manager in Manchester City's history is _____?

    A. Frank Clark

    B. Joe Royle

    C. Steve Coppell

    D. Kevin Keegan

13. Which of these former City managers managed the club for the highest number of league seasons?

    A. Wilf Wild

    B. Joe Mercer

    C. Pep Guardiola

    D. Les McDowall

14. Manchester City's first ever professional manager was named

    A. Lawrence Furniss

    B. Joshua Parlby

    C. Tom Maley

    D. Sam Ormerod

15. The first City manager to win a major trophy was named _____?

    A. Joshua Parlby

    B. Tom Maley

    C. Lawrence Furniss

    D. Sam Ormerod

16. Which former City manager guided the club to the top flight for the first time?

    A. Tom Maley

    B. Sam Ormerod

    C. Joshua Parlby

    D. Lawrence Furniss

17. Which of these managers has taken City the furthest in the UEFA Champions League?

    A. Manuel Pellegrini

    B. Pep Guardiola

    C. Roberto Mancini

    D. Mark Hughes

18. Which of these former City managers won a major trophy with the club?

    A. Ernest Mangnall

    B. Harry Newbould

    C. Sam Cowan

    D. Tony Book

19. Which of these City managers did not win a top flight title with the club?

    A. Pep Guardiola

    B. Joe Mercer

    C. Les McDowall

    D. Roberto Mancini

20. City's last promotion to the Premier League was under which of these former managers?

    A. Joe Royle

    B. Kevin Keegan

    C. Stuart Pearce

    D. Sven-Goran Eriksson

20 Trivia Answers

1. B – Roberto Mancini

2. C – Wilf Wild

3. A – Brian Horton

4. D – Joe Mercer

5. C – Roberto Mancini

6. B - Ernest Mangnall

7. A – 1946

8. B – Joe Mercer

9. D – Chilean

10. A – Alan Ball

11. C – 32 days

12. C – Steve Coppell

13. D – Les McDowall

14. A – Lawrence Furniss

15. B – Tom Maley

16. B – Sam Ormerod

17. B – Pep Guardiola

18. D – Tony Book

19. C – Les McDowall

20. B – Kevin Keegan

10 Fun Facts

1. The role of manager included secretarial duties and maintenance of the club's grounds before the creation of the Football League that heralded the professional era. It is not clear who was Manchester Citys' (then known as West Gorton or St Mark's) manager between 1882-84 as only a few records of the club's off-field activities are still obtainable.

2. City's managers in their formative years were also players. The first three known Manchester City managers (Frederick Hopkinson, Edward Kitchen, and Walter Chew) all played in St Mark's first recorded game in 1880.

3. Englishman Lawrence Furniss was City's first ever professional manager. He was in charge when the club joined the Football League Second Division in 1892. He became chairman in 1893 and with the help of his successor, secretary-manager Joshua Parlby, rebranded Ardwick AFC to Manchester City in 1894.

4. Samuel Ormerod was the first Manchester City manager to win a title and also guide the club into the top flight. He led City to the Second Division title in 1898/99 and took charge of City for the first time in the First Division in 1899/1900. He led City to comfortable mid-table finishes in their first couple of seasons in the top flight, but suffered relegation and left the club after finishing bottom in 1901/02.

5. Scotsman, Tom Maley, was the first City manager to win a major trophy. He was appointed City manager in 1902 and led them to FA Cup glory in 1903/04. He was implicated in the Football League bribery scandal in 1905 and was subsequently banned from football.

6. Former English football manager, Ernest Mangnall, joined City from rivals United in 1912, but could not replicate the success he enjoyed with the Red Devils at Manchester City. The roles of secretary and manager were separated following his departure in 1924.

7. Former British football manager, Wilf Wild, is the longest serving manager in Manchester City's history. Having held the roles of assistant manager and secretary, he combined both managerial and secretarial duties upon the departure of Peter Hodge to Leicester City. Wild won an FA Cup and City's first ever top flight title during his 14 years as City manager.

8. Scotsman, Les McDowall, has managed Manchester City in more league seasons than any other manager. He held the role for 13 years (from 1950 to 1963) and led the club to successive FA Cup finals in 1955-56. They lost 3-1 to Newcastle United in the first final, before beating Birmingham City by the same scoreline a year later.

9. Former English football manager Joe Mercer was appointed Manchester City manager in 1965. He led the club to a Second Division title, a First Division title, FA Cup, League Cup, Cup Winners Cup, and Charity Shield in a trophy-laden six-year stay at the club.

10. Pep Guardiola is the most decorated manager in Manchester City history. Since taking up the role in the summer of 2016, the Spaniard has led the club to four Premier League titles, four League Cups, one FA Cup, and two Community Shields.

GOALKEEPERS

"There have been only two world-class goalkeepers. One was Lev Yashin, the other was the German boy who played for Manchester City."

– Lev Yashin

20 Trivia Questions

1. Former City goalkeeper, David James, joined the club from _____?

    A. Everton

    B. Aston Villa

    C. Liverpool

    D. West Ham

2. How many league appearances was made by Ken Mulhearn in the 1967/68 season?

    A. 22

    B. 37

    C. 11

    D. 44

3. Former City keeper, Nicky Weaver, moved to the club from _____?

    A. Macclesfield Town

    B. Marine

    C. Middlesbrough

    D. Mansfield Town

4. From where did Manchester City goalkeeper Ederson signed for the Cityzens?

    A. Benfica

    B. Sporting Lisbon

    C. Braga

    D. Porto

5. Which of these former City goalkeepers was a paratrooper during World War II?

   A. Willy Caballero

   B. Bert Trautmann

   C. Claudio Bravo

   D. Joe Corrigan

6. How many City appearances were made by former Republic of Ireland keeper, Shay Given?

   A. 37

   B. 48

   C. 69

   D. 56

7. Nicky Weaver left City in 2007. Which club did he sign for?

   A. Coventry City

   B. Millwall

   C. Ipswich Town

   D. Charlton Athletic

8. Which goalkeeper was in goal for City's 1969 FA Cup final victory over Leicester City?

   A. Harry Dowd

   B. Ken Mulhearn

   C. Joe Corrigan

   D. Alex Williams

9. Which City goalkeeper is famous for his heroics in the 1999 play-off final victory over Gillingham?

   A. David James

   B. Nicky Weaver

   C. Alex Williams

   D. Shay Given

10. Who was City's first-choice goalkeeper when they first played in the Premier League?

    A. Bald Friedel

    B. Nicky Weaver

    C. Tony Coton

    D. Joe Hart

11. Who was the first City goalkeeper to play in the UEFA Champions League?

    A. Joe Hart

    B. Shay Given

    C. Costel Pantilmon

    D. Kasper Schmeichel

12. Manchester City signed Brazilian goalkeeper Ederson in the summer of _____?

    A. 2016

    B. 2018

    C. 2019

    D. 2017

13. Former England goalkeeper Joe Hart joined City from which of these clubs?

    A. Derby County

    B. Shrewsbury Town

    C. Hull City

    D. Exeter City

14. How many City appearances were made by former keeper Bert Trautmann?

    A. 500

    B. 342

    C. 545

    D. 450

15. Which of these keepers is the last to play for City in the UEFA Europa League?

    A. Shay Given

    B. Stuart Taylor

    C. Costel Pantilimon

    D. Joe Hart

16. Which of these former City keepers spent the longest time at the club?

    A. Joe Hart

    B. Costel Pantilimon

    C. Nicky Weaver

    D. Alex Williams

17. Which keeper was in goal for City's 1976 League Cup final victory over Newcastle United?

    A. Joe Corrigan

    B. Ken Mulhearn

    C. Bravo

    D. Keith MacRae

18. Which of these former City keepers scored a goal for the club?

    A. Joe Corrigan

    B. Keith MacRae

    C. Harry Dowd

    D. Ken Mulhearn

19. Which City keeper was in goal for the club's 1970 Cup winners Cup final victory over Gornik Zabrze?

    A. Harry Dowd

    B. Keith MacRae

    C. Ken Mulhearn

    D. Joe Corrigan

20. Which of these goalkeepers has made the most Manchester City appearances?

    A. Joe Hart

    B. Ederson

    C. Nicky Weaver

    D. Tony Coton

20 Trivia Answers

1. D – West Ham

2. B – 37

3. D- Mansfield Town

4. A – Benfica

5. B – Bert Trautmann

6. C – 69

7. D – Charlton Athletic

8. A – Harry Dowd

9. B – Nicky Weaver

10. C – Tony Coton

11. A – Joe Hart

12. D – 2017

13. B – Shrewsbury Town

14. C – 545

15. D – Joe Hart

16. C – Joe Hart

17. A – Joe Corrigan

18. C – Harry Dowd

19. D – Joe Corrigan

20. A – Joe Hart

10 Fun Facts

1. Former Manchester City goalkeeper, Frank Swift, brushed off interest from Blackpool, Blackburn, and Bradford to join Manchester City in 1933. He got a chance to impress then City manager, Wilf Wild, midway through the season when first-choice keeper, Len Langford, got injured and his replacement conceded eight goals in a game at Wolves. Swift conceded four in his first appearance against Derby but kept a clean-sheet in the next game against the same opponents. He went on to feature 375 times for the club and won a First Division title and an FA Cup before his retirement in 1949.

2. Former City goalkeeper, Joe Corrigan, joined the club in 1966, around the beginning of the club's trophy-laden era under legendary manager, Joe Mercer. At the time, Harry Dowd was the preferred option in goal, so Corrigan had to wait until 1967 to make his debut and did not become a regular first team player until 1969. He made 603 appearances for City and was part of the team that won the Cup Winners Cup and League Cup double in 1970 and the League Cup again in 1976. He transferred to the Seattle Sounders in 1983.

3. Arguably City's best ever goalkeeper, Bert Trautmann joined the club in 1949 after he turned down a chance to return to his native Germany following the end of World War II. He played for City until 1964, making 545 appearances for the club that included consecutive FA Cup finals in 1955 and 1956. He played the final 20 minutes of City's victory in the latter final over Birmingham City with a broken neck, confirmed by an X-ray three days after the final, and was named the 1956 Football Writers Association (FWA) Footballer of the Year.

4. Former City and England number one, Joe Hart, began his career at Shrewsbury Town at the age of seven. He made his debut for the first team in the 2005/06 season and put in a number of spectacular performances that drew interest from the Premier League. He was signed by City in the summer of 2006 for a deal that could reach £1.5 million depending on appearances. He was made first-choice keeper in 2007 by Sven-Goran Eriksson but had to go out on loan when City signed Shay Given from Newcastle in 2009. His first-choice status was restored under Roberto Mancini in August 2010 and he helped City end a 35-year trophy drought by winning the 2010/11 FA Cup. He added two league titles and two League Cups before he slipped down the pecking order and eventually left the club upon the arrival of Pep Guardiola.

5. Arguably the best goalkeeper that never played for England, Tony Coton was made one of the costliest goalkeepers in the country when City paid Watford around £1 million for his services in the summer of 1990. He helped City to respectable fifth-placed finishes in the league in his first two seasons and was named Manchester City's best player of the 1991/92 season. He was named City Player of the Year again in 1993/94 and made 195 competitive appearances for City before he transferred to rivals, United, as backup goalkeeper in January 1996.

6. Former City goalkeeper, Harry Dowd, made 219 appearances for the club between 1961 and 1970. He shared the goalkeeping position with Ken Mulhearn towards the end of his career in the late 1960s and made nine appearances during the 1967/68 title-winning season. He played for City in the 1969 FA Cup final over Leicester City and is one of a few City keepers to score a goal when he swapped with an outfield player following a hand injury and scored against Bury in February 1964.

7. Ex-Manchester City goalkeeper, Alex Williams, came through the club's youth ranks and eventually became first-choice shot-stopper when Joe Corrigan left. He had the position to himself for about four years before back problems set in. He moved on in 1986 having made 125 appearances.

8. Former City keeper, Ken Mulhearn, joined the club from Stockport County and played 62 times, 42 of which were league appearances made in the club's 1967/68 championship-winning season. He added a League Cup, FA Community Shield (formerly Charity Shield) , and Cup Winners Cup before he transferred to Shrewsbury Town in 1971.

9. Though former England keeper David James' stay at Manchester City was relatively short, he was a dominant figure who had a steadying impact on a club that strived to remain in the Premier League in the mid-2000s. He made 100 City appearances before he transferred to Portsmouth in 2006 for family reasons.

10. One of the club's most famous players of recent times, Nicky Weaver, joined City from Mansfield Town in 1997 and went on to spend nearly a decade with the club, though injury restricted much of his playing time. His best period at the club was between 1998 and 2002 when he played an indispensable role in the club's successive promotions from Division Two (now known as League One) to the Premier League.

DEFENDERS

"I'm never going to be someone like Vinny (Kompany).
He's been like that since he was young."

– Kevin de Bruyne

20 Trivia Questions

1. Former Belgium captain, Vincent Kompany, moved to City from which of these clubs?

    A. Anderlecht

    B. Burnley

    C. Hamburger SV

    D. Arsenal FC

2. Former Manchester City defender, Dave Ewing, was born in _____?

    A. New York

    B. Staffordshire

    C. Istanbul

    D. Perthshire

3. Manchester City's 'hardest player' as voted by the club's magazine was _____?

    A. Kevin Nolan

    B. Sam Cowan

    C. Mike Doyle

    D. Joey Barton

4. Which of these City defenders was the first to represent the club in three FA Cup finals?

    A. Dave Watson

    B. Sam Cowan

    C. Pablo Zabaleta

    D. Dave Ewing

5. Which City wingback scored a hat-trick of penalties against Everton in December 1957?

    A. Ken Barnes

    B. Sam Cowan

    C. Aleksandr Kolarov

    D. Mike Doyle

6. Which former City defender scored the equalizer during the 1970 League Cup final?

    A. Kyle Walker

    B. Micah Richards

    C. Mike Doyle

    D. Tony Book

7. How many Premier League clean sheets were kept by Richard Dunne during his time at City?

    A. 20

    B. 39

    C. 68

    D. 61

8. The only City player selected in the 2012/13 PFA Team of the Season was _____?

   A. Vincent Kompany

   B. Pablo Zabaleta

   C. Joleon Lescott

   D. Aleksandar Kolarov

9. Argentina defender Nicolas Otamendi, joined City from which of these teams?

   A. Valencia

   B. Benfica

   C. Porto

   D. River Plate

10. The second defender to represent City in three FA Cup finals was _____?

    A. Nicolas Otamendi

    B. John Stones

    C. Vincent Kompany

    D. Pablo Zabaleta

11. Portugal defender, Joao Cancelo, joined City in a deal that involved which other defender?

    A. Ruben Dias

    B. Aymeric Laporte

    C. Aleksandar Zinchenko

    D. Danilo

12. Which of these City defenders did not join the club from a Premier League side?

    A. Bacary Sagna

    B. Richard Dunne

    C. Aleksandar Kolarov

    D. Gael Clichy

13. Which of these City defenders was the first to arrive at the club?

    A. John Stones

    B. Kyle Walker

    C. Aymeric Laporte

    D. Ruben Dias

14. Which City defender left the club for Portland Timbers in 1979?

    A. Tony Book

    B. Willie Donachie

    C. Dave Watson

    D. Ken Barnes

15. Which of these former City defenders went on to manage the club?

    A. Sam Cowan

    B. Mike Doyle

    C. Richard Dunne

    D. Dave Ewing

16. What is the nationality of former City defender, Gael Clichy?

    A. English

    B. Dutch

    C. Welsh

    D. French

17. City's first UEFA Champions League goal was scored by which of these players?

    A. Vincent Kompany

    B. Aleksandar Kolarov

    C. Joleon Lescott

    D. Stefan Savic

18. How many goals were scored by former City defender Micah Richards during his time at the club?

    A. 18

    B. 10

    C. 9

    D. 17

19. Argentine defender Pablo Zabaleta, joined Manchester City in the summer of_____?

    A. 2009

    B. 2008

    C. 2013

    D. 2010

20. What is the nationality of former City defender, Stefan Savic?

    A. Croatian

    B. Serbian

    C. Bosnian

    D. Montenegrin

20 Trivia Answers

1. C – Hamburger SV

2. D – Perthshire

3. C – Mike Doyle

4. B – Sam Cowan

5. A – Ken Barnes

6. C – Mike Doyle

7. D – 61

8. B – Pablo Zabaleta

9. A – Valencia

10. C – Vincent Kompany

11. D – Danilo

12. C – Aleksandar Kolarov

13. A – John Stones

14. B – Willie Donachie

15. A – Sam Cowan

16. D – French

17. B – Aleksandar Kolarov

18. B – 10

19. B – 2008

20. D – Montenegrin

10 Fun Facts

1. Perthshire-born former City defender Dave Ewing was scouted by the club while he was at Luncarty Juniors. He was signed to Manchester City in June 1949 but he had to wait another three years before he was handed a first team debut. He scored a club record 10 own goals across his 279 City appearances and helped the team win the 1955/56 FA Cup before leaving for Crewe Alexandra in 1962.

2. Former Manchester City defender, Mike Doyle, joined the club as a youngster in May 1962. He scored 41 goals in his 570 appearances for the club and was voted as the 'club's 'hardest player in City's official magazine. He scored the equalizer in City's 1970 League Cup final victory over West Bromwich Albion and captained the side to another League Cup glory in 1976. He was transferred to Stoke City in 1978 having won eight major honours with City.

3. Scottish defender, Willie Donachie, joined Manchester City through the club's youth system in 1968 and made his first team debut in February 1970. His appearances were few and far between until he was selected in the starting eleven for the last 11 matches of the 1970/71 season. He made the left back position his own for the next eight seasons, missing only a handful of league games between 1973 and 1977. He won the League Cup with City in 1976 before he moved to Portland Timbers in 1979.

4. Described as "the best uncapped wing half to have played in English football" by former teammate Denis Law, Ken Barnes joined Manchester City for only 750 pounds from non-league side Stafford Rangers in May 1950. He played only one game for City's senior team in his first four seasons at the club. He was promoted to the first team ahead of the start of the 1954/55 season and became club captain when Roy Paul retired in 1957. He played 258 league games for City and scored 18 goals including a hattrick of penalties in a 6-2 league win over Everton in December 1957.

5. Former City centre back, Sam Cowan, joined the club from Doncaster Rovers in 1924 and was renowned for his astonishing leadership and heading ability, which led former teammate Matt busby to assert that "Cowan could head a ball as far as most of us could kick it." He made 407 appearances for City and was the first to represent the club in three FA Cup finals, losing the first two before winning on the third occasion.

6. Former England central defender, Dave Watson, joined City for a fee of 175,000 pounds in the summer of 1975 from Sunderland, whom he had helped win the 1973 FA Cup final against Leeds United. His formidable partnership with Mike Doyle helped City to a League Cup success in 1976 and they missed out on the First Division title by just a single point in the following season. He left the club at the end of his fourth season having made 188 appearances in all competitions.

7. Former City right back, Tony Book, spent most of his football career in non-league football with Bath City, his hometown club. He was transferred to City at the age of 31 in 1966 and was made captain soon afterwards. He made 315 appearances for City and captained the club to five major honours before he was appointed manager in 1974, a role he held for the next five years. He shared the 1969 FWA Footballer of the Year with former Tottenham defender Dave Mackay.

8. Former Republic of Ireland centre back , Richard Dunne, scored eight goals across his 352 appearances for City between 2000 and 2009. He was signed from Everton for £3.5 million and became club captain in 2005. He was named Manchester City Player of the Season four times in succession, the only City player to earn the honour, and has received a joint Premier League record eight red cards, along with Duncan Ferguson and Patrick Vieira. He has also scored a Premier League record of 10 own goals across his spells with Everton, Manchester City, Aston Villa, and QPR.

9. Argentina Summer Olympics gold medalist, Pablo Zabaleta, moved from Espanyol to Manchester City in the summer of 2008. He made his City debut in September 2008 against Chelsea and scored the club's first goal in the memorable Premier League final day victory over QPR in the 2011/12 season. He was the only City player in the 2012/13 PFA Team of the Year and was named Etihad Manchester

City Player of the Year for the same season. He won all the domestic honours in English football and was described as a "legend" by Pep Guardiola when he made his 333rd and final appearance for the club. He was awarded with a City shirt with the number 333 emblazoned at the back and a lifetime season ticket.

10. Former Belgian centre back , Vincent Kompany joined Manchester City in 2008 and went on to feature prominently for eleven seasons, eight as club captain. He scored 20 goals across his 360 appearances and won four Premier League titles, four League Cups, two FA Cups and two Community Shields before he left to spend the final season of his career at Belgian side Anderlecht.

MIDFIELDERS

"When I first came to Maine Road, it was good to find players of Alan Oakes' quality already here. He is one of the most conscientious trainers I have ever worked with… always in top class physical condition and always willing to learn and improve."

– Malcolm Allison

20 Trivia Questions

1. Where was former Manchester City midfielder, Fernando, signed from?

   A. Porto

   B. Galatasaray

   C. Sevilla

   D. Vila Nova

2. Which of these former City midfielders scored the most goals for the club?

   A. Georgi Kinkladze

   B. Colin Bell

   C. Alan Oakes

   D. Asa Hartford

3. The first graduate of City's youth academy that broke into the first team was _____?

   A. Phil Foden

   B. Jadon Sancho

   C. Shaun Wright-Phillips

   D. Paul Lake

4. Ivorian midfielder Yaya Toure played his final City game against _____?

   A. Huddersfield Town

   B. Everton

   C. Aston Villa

   D. Brighton

5. Colin Bell featured for City for the last time in a Maine Road defeat against
    _____?

    A. Arsenal

    B. Chelsea

    C. Aston Villa

    D. Liverpool

6. Portuguese midfielder, Bernardo Silva, joined City from which of these clubs?

    A. Benfica

    B. Monaco

    C. Porto

    D. Braga

7. Brazilian midfielder Fernandinho , moved to City in the year _____?

    A. 2013

    B. 2009

    C. 2015

    D. 2012

8. How many City appearances were made by former Spain midfielder, David
    Silva?

    A. 330

    B. 532

    C. 234

    D. 436

9. The West Stand at Manchester City's stadium has been named after which of
    these former midfielders?

    A. Alan Oakes

    B. Colin Bell

    C. Paul Lake

    D. Neil McNab

10. What is the nationality of former City midfielder, Georgi Kinkladze?

    A. Montenegrin

    B. Italian

    C. Georgian

    D. Armenian

11. Which of these City midfielders is a multi-recipient of the PFA and Premier League Player of the Season awards?

    A. David Silva

    B. Kevin de Bruyne

    C. Yaya Toure

    D. Fernandinho

12. Which former City midfielder scored the first goal in the 10-1 win over Huddersfield in 1987?

    A. Graham Baker

    B. Paul Lake

    C. Neil McNab

    D. Kevin Langley

13. Which former City midfielder was sent off in City's 3-2 win over QPR in May 2012?

    A. Joey Barton

    B. Shaun Wright-Phillips

    C. Yaya Toure

    D. Nigel de Jong

14. Spanish midfielder, Rodri, joined Manchester City from which of these clubs?

    A. Villareal

    B. Valencia

    C. Athletic Bilbao

    D. Atletico Madrid

15. Former Netherlands midfielder, Nigel de Jong, played for City for how many years?

    A. 3

    B. 2

    C. 5

    D. 1

16. Yaya Toure's 2011 FA Cup final winner was scored against which of these teams?

    A. Sheffield United

    B. Southampton

    C. Stoke City

    D. Sunderland

17. Former City midfielder Georgi Kinkladze moved to the club from _____?

    A. Dinamo Tbilisi

    B. Dinamo Moscow

    C. Dinamo Zagreb

    D. Dinamo Kyiv

18. What was the transfer fee involved in England midfielder Kalvin Phillips' move to City?

    A. £40 million

    B. £42 million

    C. £48 million

    D. £50 million

19. Former City midfielder, Stephen Ireland, left the club in the year _____?

    A. 2005

    B. 2009

    C. 2013

    D. 2010

20. What is the nationality of former City midfielder, Dietmar Hamann?

    A. Dutch

    B. German

    C. Austrian

    D. Swiss

20 Trivia Answers

1. A – Porto

2. B – Colin Bell

3. D – Paul Lake

4. D – Brighton

5. C – Aston Villa

6. B – Monaco

7. A – 2013

8. D – 436

9. B – Colin Bell

10. C – Georgian

11. B – Kevin de Bruyne

12. C – Neil McNab

13. A – Joey Baton

14. D – Atletico Madrid

15. A – 3

16. C – Stoke City

17. A – Dinamo Tbilisi

18. B – 42 million pounds

19. D – 2010

20. B - German

10 Fun Facts

1. Arguably Manchester City's best player of the modern era, Spanish World Cup winner, David Silva, joined the club from Valencia in the summer of 2010. He helped end City 35-year major trophy drought in his first season, and went on to make a total of 436 City appearances in which he scored 77 goals and won 11 major honours. He left the club at the expiration of his contract in 2020 to join Real Sociedad.

2. . Yaya Toure made a £24 million move from Barcelona to Manchester City in the summer of 2010 joining his older brother Kolo, who was already at the club. He contributed immensely as the club ended a 35-year major honour drought by winning the 2010/11 FA Cup, with Yaya Toure netting winners in the semifinal and final against Manchester United and Stoke City respectively. He scored 82 goals in his 316 Manchester City appearances and was named African Footballer of the Year four times between 2011 and 2014. He left City in 2018 having won seven major honours with the club.

3. Eyebrows were raised when City paid out a club record fee to sign Belgium midfielder Kevin de Bruyne in 2015, considering he had flopped so spectacularly at fellow Premier League side Chelsea not too long ago. The Belgian soon laid those doubts to rest with some of the most majestic performances the Premier League has ever seen, leading many to proclaim him the league's greatest ever midfielder. So far, De Bruyne has scored 89 goals in 332 competitive City appearances and has won four Premier League titles, five League Cups, and one FA Cup along with several individual accolades.

4. Brazilian midfielder, Fernandinho, joined City in 2013 having recently starred with Ukrainian club Shaktar Donetsk in the previous season's UEFA Champions League. He made an instant impact at City screening the back four so efficiently and helping the team wrestle back the Premier League title from rivals United

in his first season at the club. Prior to his departure in 2022, he made 383 appearances for the club and scored 26 goals among which was Manchester City's Goal of the Season for the 2017/18 season. He held the role of club captain in his final two seasons at the club where he won 12 major honours.

5. English midfielder, Colin "the King" Bell, joined City from Bury FC for 47,500 pounds in 1966, with the club in English football's second tier at the time. He helped City win promotion to the top flight and then end a 31-year wait for the championship in his first three seasons at the club. He scored 153 goals in his 501 appearances for City and left the club in 1979 having collected six major honours. The West Stand at the City of Manchester Stadium (Etihad Stadium) has been named after him since 2004.

6. Georgi Kinkladze was a cult hero at Dinamo Tbilisi due to his exquisite dribbling ability and occasional spectacular goals before his move to Manchester City in 1995. He wowed fans with his amazing skills and was a flicker of light in a dark 1995/96 season that eventually ended with relegation from the top flight. He scored 22 goals in 121 appearances and was voted City Player of the Year in his first two seasons, before a third straight relegation proved too much to bear for the talented Georgian midfielder, who transferred to Ajax in 1998.

7. The seventeen years English midfielder Alan Oakes spent at Manchester City between 1959 to 1976 were sufficient to make him one of the club's most decorated players and its record appearance holder. Having joined the club as an amateur in 1958, he turned professional a year later and went on to become an integral part of the club's glorious era of the late 60s and early 70s. He scored 34 goals in a club record 680 appearances before he moved to Chester City in 1976.

8. English winger, Shaun Wright-Phillips, joined City initially as a youth prospect from Nottingham Forest when he was only 17 years old. He became the first graduate of City's youth system to break into the senior side, making his debut in a League Cup tie against Burnley in 1999. He helped City to two promotions from Division Two to the Premier League and was voted as the club's Young Player of the Year for four straight years between 2000 and 2003. He left City for Chelsea in 2005 but returned three years later for a second spell that lasted for three seasons. He left the club for a second time to join QPR in 2011. He scored 46 goals in 275 appearances across his two spells and was voted Manchester City Player of the Year in 2004.

9. Arguably Manchester City's best player of the 1980s, Scottish midfielder, Neil McNab joined the club from Brighton for 35,000 pounds in 1983. He scored the first goal in a 10-1 victory over Huddersfield and was voted City Player of the Year for the 1986/87 and 1988/89 seasons. He scored 19 goals in 266 appearances and is credited for inspiring a youthful City side to promotion to the English top flight in 1989, before he was transferred to Tranmere Rovers in 1990.

10. Former Scotland midfielder, Asa Hartford, made 321 appearances and scored 36 goals across two spells with Manchester City that spanned eight seasons. The exquisitely strong and talented midfielder joined the club initially from West Bromwich Albion in 1974 and helped City to a League Cup win in 1976. He left the club in the season of 1978/1979 but returned after only two years to spend three more seasons before moving on to Norwich City in 1984.

FORWARDS

*"Of all the opponents I faced I particularly remember
Doherty, who was unplayable on his day. He was built
like a greyhound, very fast and elusive but with stamina
too. He had a Rolls-Royce engine in him."*

– Joe Mercer

20 Trivia Questions

1. Which national team did former City striker, Shaun Goater, play for?

    A. Jamaica

    B. Bermuda

    C. Sao Tome

    D. Haiti

2. How many goals were scored by City's all-time top goalscorer Sergio Aguero for the club?

    A. 230

    B. 225

    C. 260

    D. 275

3. Former City forward, Rodney Marsh, joined the club in 1972 from _____?

    A. Brighton

    B. Hull City

    C. Wigan

    D. QPR

4. What is the nationality of former City forward Uwe Rosler?

    A. Austrian

    B. Finnish

    C. Dutch

    D. German

5. Former City striker Edin Dzeko joined the club in 2010 from _____?

    A. Werder Bremen

    B. Wolfsburg

    C. Stuttgart

    D. Hamburg

6. Irish striker, Niall Quinn, joined Manchester City from Arsenal in _____?

    A. 1990

    B. 1991

    C. 1989

    D. 1988

7. How many goals were scored for City by former forward, Neil Young?

    A. 108

    B. 110

    C. 112

    D. 109

8. How many games did City's record goalscorer Sergio Aguero play for the club?

    A. 360

    B. 380

    C. 390

    D. 370

9. Which of these former City forwards was not on target in City's 6-1 win at Old Trafford in October 2011?

    A. Mario Balotelli

    B. Carlos Tevez

    C. Sergio Aguero

    D. Edin Dzeko

10. Which of these City forwards played no part in the 2019 FA Cup final victory over Watford?

    A. Sergio Aguero

    B. Riyad Mahrez

    C. Gabriel Jesus

    D. Raheem Sterling

11. Former Manchester City forward, Tommy Johnson, was sold to which of these clubs?

    A. Arsenal

    B. Liverpool

    C. Chelsea

    D. Everton

12. From which club did former City and Brazil forward, Jo, join City?

    A. Everton

    B. Atletico Mineiro

    C. CSKA Moscow

    D. Internacional

13. How many goals were scored for City by former England forward, Francis Lee?

    A. 118

    B. 148

    C. 178

    D. 208

14. Which of these former City forwards has the second most goals for the club?

    A. Eric Brook

    B. Raheem Sterling

    C. Tommy Johnson

    D. Neil Young

15. How many goals were scored for City by former forward, Billy Gillespie?

    A. 122

    B. 112

    C. 132

    D. 142

16. Sergio Aguero became City's all-time highest goalscorer in a game against_____?

    A. Schalke 04

    B. Shaktar Donetsk

    C. Barcelona

    D. Napoli

17. How many appearances were made for Manchester City by former forward, Tommy Johnson?

    A. 355

    B. 344

    C. 334

    D. 324

18. Which of these former City forwards is the club's fifth all-time highest goalscorer?

    A. Tommy Johnson

    B. Joe Hayes

    C. Francis Lee

    D. Tommy Bromwell

19. Zimbabwean forward, Benjani Mwaruwari, was signed by City from which of these clubs?

    A. Sunderland

    B. Blackburn Rovers

    C. Portsmouth

    D. Chippa United

20. Which of these former City forwards scored the most goals for the club?

    A. Wilfred Bony

    B. Mario Balotelli

    C. Alvaro Negredo

    D. Stevan Jovetic

20 Trivia Answers

1. B – Bermuda

2. C – 260

3. D – QPR

4. D – German

5. B – Wolfsburg

6. A – 1990

7. C – 108

8. C – 390

9. B – Carlos Tevez

10. A – Sergio Aguero

11. D – Everton

12. C – CSKA Moscow

13. B – 148

14. A – Eric Brook

15. C – 132

16. D – Napoli

17. A – 355

18. B – Joe Hayes

19. C – Portsmouth

20. B – Mario Balotelli

10 Fun Facts

1. Argentine striker, Sergio Aguero, is the most prolific player in the history of Manchester City. He scored 260 goals during the ten years he spent at the club between 2011 and 2021. He broke Erik Brook's record of 177 City goals which has stood since 1940 during a 4-2 City win at Napoli in the UEFA Champions League.

2. Sergio Aguero became the Premier League player with the most hattricks (12) in the competition's history when he scored three times at Aston Villa in January 2020 to surpass Alan Shearer's record of 11.

3. Sergio Aguero is the most prolific foreign player in Premier League history. He overtook French forward Thierry Henry's record of 175 goals during a 6-0 win at Aston Villa where he netted a hattrick. He had a total of 184 Premier League goals when he left City for Barcelona in 2021.

4. No player has scored as many goals in a single season for the club as former Manchester City forward Tommy Johnson. The English forward scored 38 times for the club in the 1928/29 season. He is also the club's third all-time goalscorer with 166 goals. His popularity with the City fans led to protests when he was sold to Everton in 1930.

5. Former City and Scotland forward Denis Law's six goals had given City a 6-2 lead against Luton Town in an FA Cup tie in January 1961, but the game was abandoned before its completion due to torrential rain. The rearranged game ended 3-1 in favour of Luton, with Law getting City's only goal.

6. No player has scored in as many consecutive games for Manchester City as Erling Haaland. The Norway striker scored in ten successive games for the club between August and October 2022.

7. Former City forward, Sergio Aguero, jointly shares the record for the most goals scored by a player in a single Premier League match. He scored an incredible five times during a 6-1 home win over Newcastle United in October 2015.

8. Former City forward, Fred Tilson, is the club's most prolific player in the FA Cup. The English centre forward scored 21 times in the FA Cup for City during his decade-long stay at the club.

9. Older City fans regard former City forward, Peter Doherty, higher than Colin Bell and some even argue that the Irish-born forward is City's greatest ever player. Doherty scored 80 goals in 131 appearances and led City to their first ever top flight title in 1937 before his time at the club was curtailed by the Second World War.

10. English forward, Francis Lee, joined Manchester City for a then club record of 60,000 pounds in 1967. He scored one of the goals in City's 4 -3 final matchday victory over Newcastle United that sealed the club's second top flight title. He is also City's highest goalscorer in the Community Shield with three goals.

CAPTAINS

"Let's face it, I'm a City fanatic. I'm the guy in the terraces that has been given the chance to put down his rattle and step out for the team he loves."

– Mike Doyle

20 Trivia Questions

1. Who was the first City captain to win a major trophy?

   A. Lot Jones

   B. Billy Meredith

   C. Vincent Kompany

   D. Max Woosnam

2. Which of these players captained City in the 1934 FA Cup final?

   A. Les McDowall

   B. Jimmy McMullan

   C. Charlie Pringle

   D. Sam Cowan

3. Which of these former City captains did not go on to manage the club?

   A. Ken Barnes

   B. Sam Cowan

   C. Les McDowall

   D. Tony Book

4. Which of these players was City's captain at the start of the Premier League in 1992?

   A. Steve Redmond

   B. Keith Curle

   C. Terry Phelan

   D. Kit Symons

5. Who was City's skipper in their first ever UEFA Champions League game?

    A. Vincent Kompany

    B. Edin Dzeko

    C. Pablo Zabaleta

    D. Carlos Tevez

6. Who was City's captain prior to the appointment of Richard Dunne to the role?

    A. Ali Bernabia

    B. Sylvian Distin

    C. Stuart Pearce

    D. Alfie Haaland

7. Which of these former City players was the club's first English captain?

    A. Max Woosman

    B. Sam Cowan

    C. Frank Swift

    D. Eli Fletcher

8. The only African player that has ever been appointed City captain is _____?

    A. Benjani Mwaruwari

    B. Kolo Toure

    C. Yaya Toure

    D. Emmanuel Adebayor

9. Manchester City's last promotion to the Premier League was achieved under the captaincy of_____?

    A. Stuart Pearce

    B. Alfie Haaland

    C. Andy Morrison

    D. Ali Bernabia

10. Who captained City in their 1999 Second Division playoff victory over Gillingham?

   A. Shaun Goater

   B. Andy Morrison

   C. Michael Brown

   D. Paul Dickov

11. Who was the club's captain before football was paused due to World War I?

   A. Billy Meredith

   B. Eli Fletcher

   C. Lot Jones

   D. Max Wossman

12. Which of these former City captains led the club to its first Football League Cup?

   A. Mike Doyle

   B. Colin Bell

   C. Johnny Crossan

   D. Tony Book

13. Which of these players led City out as captain in the 2021 UEFA Champions League final?

   A. Kevin de Bruyne

   B. Ilkay Gundogan

   C. John Stones

   D. Raheem Sterling

14. Which of these former City players won a major honor as the club's captain?

   A. Richard Dunne

   B. Mike Doyle

   C. Rodri

   D. Kolo Toure

15. Which trophy did David Silva win during his solitary season as City captain?

    A. FA Cup

    B. League Cup

    C. Premier League

    D. Champions League

16. Who captained City in the 1981 FA Cup final defeat to Spurs?

    A. Roy Paul

    B. Kevin Doyle

    C. Paul Power

    D. Colin Bell

17. Which of these players was City's captain in the first season after World War II?

    A. Sam Cowan

    B. Sam Barkas

    C. Les McDowall

    D. Frank Swift

18. Which of these players was City's captain when the club returned to the Premier League in 2002?

    A. Joey Barton

    B. Erling Haaland

    C. Alfie Haaland

    D. Ali Bernabia

19. Which former City player captained the club to glory in the 1970 Cup Winners Cup final?

    A. Tony Flowers

    B. Tommy Booth

    C. Tony Book

    D. Colin Bell

20. Which of these former City players was never appointed as club captain?

    A. Paul Power

    B. Alan Oakes

    C. Colin Bell

    D. Dave Watson

20 Trivia Answers

1. B – Billy Meredith

2. D – Sam Cowan

3. A – Ken Barnes

4. C- Terry Phelan

5. A – Vincent Kompany

6. B – Sylvian Distin

7. D – Eli Fletcher

8. B – Kolo Toure

9. A – Stuart Pearce

10. B – Andy Morrison

11. C – Lot Jones

12. D – Tony Book

13. A – Kevin de Bruyne

14. B – Mike Doyle

15. B – League Cup

16. C – Paul Power

17. B – Sam Barkas

18. D – Ali Bernabia

19. C – Tony Book

20. B – Alan Oakes

10 Fun Facts

1. Belgian defender, Vincent Kompany, is Manchester City's most decorated captain. He joined the club from Hamburg in the summer of 2008 and was made captain in 2011. He led the club to four Premier League titles, four League Cups, and two FA Cups as part of an unprecedented treble of domestic trophies in his final season at the club.

2. Tony Book was almost 32 years old when he made the move from Plymouth Argyle to Manchester City in 1966. He won the club's inaugural Player of the Year award and was made captain of the team that won four major honours between 1968 and 1970.

3. Former Manchester City forward, Billy Meredith, was the first captain to lead the club to a major trophy. He scored the only goal in City's 1-0 victory over Bolton Wanderers in the 1904 FA Cup final.

4. No player has won as many consecutive Manchester City Player of the Year awards as former captain, Richard Dunne. The Irish centreback joined the club in 2000 from Everton and was named captain in 2006. He won four successive Manchester City Player of the Year awards between 2005 and 2008.

5. Former City leftback and captain, Paul Power, played 445 games for the club between 1975 and 1986. He was named captain in 1979 and led the club to three Wembley finals, including the 1981 FA Cup final defeat to Tottenham Hotspur.

6. Former Wales defender, Roy Paul, joined City following their relegation to the Second Division in 1950/51. He helped the club regain its top flight status and as captain led the club to successive FA Cup finals in 1955-56. City lost the first final to Newcastle United but won the second against Birmingham City.

7. Former City defender, Mike Doyle, joined the club as an amateur in 1962 and made his first team debut in the 2-2 draw at Cardiff City in March 1964. He helped City regain their top flight status and played 45 games in the title -winning 1967/68 season. He was named City captain in 1975 and led the club to a second League Cup in 1976.

8. Brazilian midfielder, Fernandinho, spent his final two seasons as City captain following the departures of Vincent Kompany and David Silva in 2019 and 2020 respectively. He led the club to successive Premier League titles albeit playing a bit-part role due to the presence of the much younger Rodri in the team.

9. Scottish centre back , Andy Morrison, played only 48 games for City across his four-year stay at the club but made such a significant impact that he is considered among the club's best ever captains. He joined the club in 1998 following their relegation to the third tier of English football and led them back to the Premier League before he left in 2001 .

10. Spanish World Cup winner, David Silva, was appointed as Manchester City captain in his tenth and final season at the club following the exit of City legend, Vincent Kompany, at the end of the previous season. The Spaniard led City to a third successive League Cup trophy, beating Aston Villa 2-1 in the final.

TITLES

"There has been a lot of expectation on Manchester City and with the spending they have done they have to win something. Sometimes you have a noisy neighbor and have to live with it."

– Sir Alex Ferguson

20 Trivia Questions

1. Manchester City won a first ever title in _____?

    A. 1900

    B. 1889

    C. 1899

    D. 1901

2. Which of these was the first ever title won by Manchester City?

    A. FA Cup

    B. League Cup

    C. Community Shield

    D. Second Division

3. Which club did Manchester City beat to win its first major title?

    A. Blackburn Rovers

    B. Bristol City

    C. Birmingham City

    D. Bolton Wanderers

4. How many points were amassed by City when they won a first top flight title in 1936/37?

    A. 42

    B. 57

    C. 50

    D. 63

5. City won the 1970 Cup Winners Cup final. Who were the opponents?

    A. Crvena Zvezda

    B. Steaua Bucharest

    C. Gornik Zabrze

    D. Bate Borisov

6. Manchester City's first ever FA Cup was won in _____?

    A. 1904

    B. 1922

    C. 1970

    D. 1935

7. City won a fourth FA Cup in 1969 by defeating which of these clubs?

    A. Portsmouth

    B. Bolton Wanderers

    C. Leicester City

    D. Birmingham City

8. The goal that won City a first ever major title was scored by which of these players?

    A. Shaun Goater

    B. Sandy Turnbull

    C. Frank Booth

    D. Billy Meredith

9. Who scored the goal that won City the 1969 FA Cup final?

    A. Neil Young

    B. Lee Francis

    C. Colin Bell

    D. Alan Oakes

10. When did City win the FA Community/Charity Shield for the first time?

    A. 1998

    B. 1937

    C. 1968

    D. 1905

11. Which club apart from Manchester City has won four consecutive League Cups?

    A. Arsenal

    B. Manchester United

    C. Chelsea

    D. Liverpool

12. City's only defeat in a League Cup final came in which of these seasons?

    A. 1973/74

    B. 1965/66

    C. 1970/71

    D. 1995/96

13. When did Manchester City win their last FA Community Shield?

    A. 2017

    B. 2018

    C. 2019

    D. 2020

14. Which of these former City players did not score a winning goal in a major cup final?

    A. Neil Young

    B. Vincent Kompany

    C. Billy Meredith

    D. Yaya Toure

15. Which of these former City players has not scored a brace in a FA Cup final?

    A. Fred Tilson

    B. Raheem Sterling

    C. Gabriel Jesus

    D. Sergio Aguero

16. The winning goal that won City's first ever League Cup was scored in extra time by _____?

    A. Kevin Doyle

    B. Glyn Pardoe

    C. Neil Young

    D. Lee Francis

17. Which team contested and lost the 2019 FA Cup final against Manchester City?

    A. Wolves

    B. Brighton

    C. Watford

    D. Everton

18. Manchester City won the 2018/19 FA Community Shield against which of these teams?

    A. Chelsea

    B. Arsenal

    C. Liverpool

    D. Manchester United

19. Manchester City's fifth FA Cup was won in 2011. Who were the opponents in the final?

    A. Sheffield United

    B. Sunderland

    C. Southampton

    D. Stoke City

20. Which of these teams has not lost a major cup final against Manchester City?

    A. Portsmouth

    B. West Bromwich Albion

    C. Newcastle United

    D. Wigan Athletic

20 Trivia Answers

1. C – 1899

2. D – Second Division

3. D – Bolton Wanderers

4. B – 1957

5. C – Gornik Zabrze

6. A – 1904

7. C – Leicester City

8. D – Billy Meredith

9. A – Neil Young

10. B – 1937

11. D – Liverpool

12. A – 1973/74

13. C – 2019

14. B – Vincent Kompany

15. D – Sergio Aguero

16. B -Glyn Pardoe

17. C – Watford

18. A – Chelsea

19. D – Stoke City

20. D – Wigan Athletic

10 Fun Facts

1. Manchester City's first ever title was won in 1899 when the club finished top of the Football League Second Division with 52 points (two points for a win) from 34 games.

2. Manchester City won their first ever major title in the 1903/04 season. A goal from captain Billy Meredith helped the club beat Bolton Wanderers 1-0 in the 1904 FA Cup final.

3. Manchester City won a first top flight championship title in 1936/37 when they finished top of the Football League First Division. The club won 22 out of its 42 league matches and amassed at total of 57 points (two points for a win).

4. Manchester City won a second FA Cup title in the 1933/34 season when they beat Portsmouth 2-1 in the final thanks to a Fred Tilson brace in the final 20 minutes of the game after Portsmouth's Septimus Rutherford had given his side the lead near the half hour mark.

5. Manchester City tasted success in European club competition for the first time when they beat Polish side Gornik Zabrze 2-1 in Vienna to win the 1969/70 UEFA Cup Winners Cup. City's goals were scored by Neil Young and Francis Lee in the first half.

6. Manchester City won their first ever Football League Cup in 1970 when they beat West Bromwich Albion 2-1 in the final at Wembley. Albion's Jeff Astle scored the opener to become the first player to score in both the FA Cup final and League Cup final at Wembley. City turned the game around with goals from Mike Doyle and Glyn Pardoe.

7. Manchester City have won the FA Community/ Charity Shield on six occasions, first winning it in 1937 shortly after the club won the First Division title for the first time.

8. Manchester City matched Liverpool's haul of four successive League Cup triumphs when they beat Chelsea on penalties to win a fourth consecutive League Cup in the 2020/2021 season. City have won the League Cup eight times, one short of Liverpool's record nine triumphs in the competition.

9. Manchester City completed an unprecedented clean-sweep of domestic trophies in the 2018/19 season when the club won the Premier League, FA Cup, and League Cup in addition to the FA Community Shield they had won at the start of that season.

10. Manchester City reached successive FA Cup finals for the first time in the 1954/55 and 1955/56 season. They lost the first final but won the second. Overall, City have played in the FA Cup final eleven times and have emerged winners on six occasions.

MEMORABLE GAMES

"The only thing I've ever been able to remember about that day with clarity is that the moment Sergio took a touch, I knew he'd score."

– Martin Tyler

20 Trivia Questions

1. Which City player was not on the score sheet during the club's 4-3 memorable win at Newcastle United in May 1968?

    A. Francis Lee

    B. Neil Young

    C. Mike Summerbee

    D. Tony Coleman

2. Which player scored the opening goal in City's 4-1 win over Spurs in December 1967?

    A. Colin Bell

    B. Tony Coleman

    C. Jimmy Greaves

    D. Terry Venables

3. Which team played out a 5-3 thriller against City in the 2016/17 UEFA Champions League Round of 16 first leg?

    A. Lyon

    B. Monaco

    C. Lille

    D. Marseille

4. City's 4-3 loss at Liverpool in the 2017/18 Premier League was played in the month of _____?

   A. January

   B. February

   C. April

   D. March

5. Where did City's 1970 UEFA Cup Winners Cup final victory take place?

   A. Amsterdam

   B. Paris

   C. Berlin

   D. Vienna

6. What was the full time scoreline of City's 1999 Second Division playoff final against Gillingham?

   A. 1-1

   B. 3-3

   C. 2-2

   D. 4-4

7. Which of these City players did not score a goal in the 4-3 win over Spurs in the 2018/19 UEFA Champions League quarterfinal second leg?

   A. Raheem Sterling

   B. David Silva

   C. Sergio Aguero

   D. Bernardo Silva

8. Which former England player scored the winning goal in City's 4-3 loss at Manchester United in September 2009?

    A. Michael Owen

    B. Michael Carrick

    C. Wayne Rooney

    D. Rio Ferdinand

9. City won 6-1 at Old Trafford in the 2011/12 Premier League season. In what month was the match played?

    A. September

    B. October

    C. November

    D. December

10. Which of these players scored a goal in City's 2019 FA Cup final victory after coming in as a substitute?

    A. David Silva

    B. Gabriel Jesus

    C. Kevin de Bruyne

    D. Raheem Sterling

11. City's 4-3 win at Spurs in the 2003/04 FA Cup Fourth Round took place in the month of _____?

    A. January

    B. March

    C. April

    D. February

12. Which of these City players scored a goal in the club's first ever UEFA Champions League win against Villareal in October 2011?

    A. Aleksandar Kolarov

    B. Gael Clichy

    C. Yaya Toure

    D. Sergio Aguero

13. At what stage of the 2010/11 FA Cup did City beat rivals United 1-0?

    A. Final

    B. Semifinal

    C. Quarterfinal

    D. Fourth Round

14. Which City player was not on the score sheet in the 2011/12 Premier League final day victory over QPR?

    A. Pablo Zabaleta

    B. Edin Dzeko

    C. Mario Balotelli

    D. Sergio Aguero

15. Which former City player scored in the 1-1 tie against Liverpool in the 2016 League Cup final?

    A. Sergio Aguero

    B. Fernandinho

    C. Yaya Toure

    D. Nicolas Otamendi

16. Which of these London-based teams lost the 2018 League Cup final 0-3 against City?

    A. Arsenal

    B. Chelsea

    C. Tottenham

    D. West Ham

17. City inflicted Liverpool's only defeat of the 2018/19 Premier League season on the Reds in the month of _____?

    A. December

    B. February

    C. March

    D. January

18. What was the scoreline of the 2019 League Cup final penalty shootout between City and Chelsea?

    A. 3-2

    B. 5-4

    C. 4-3

    D. 5-3

19. Vincent Kompany's last ever City goal was scored in a 1-0 Premier League victory against

    A. Tottenham Hotspur

    B. Brighton

    C. Huddersfield Town

    D. Leicester City

20. Who did Manchester City record their first ever Premier League win against?

    A. QPR

    B. Norwich City

    C. Blackburn Rovers

    D. Middlesbrough

20 Trivia Answers

1. D – Tony Coleman

2. C – Jimmy Greaves

3. B – Monaco

4. A – January

5. D – Vienna

6. C – 2-2

7. B – David Silva

8. A – Michael Owen

9. B – October

10. C – Kevin de Bruyne

11. D – February

12. D – Sergio Aguero

13. B – Semifinal

14. C – Mario Balotelli

15. B – Fernandinho

16. A – Arsenal

17. D – January

18. C - 4-3

19. D – Leicester City

20. B – Norwich City

10 Fun Facts

1. Manchester City went into the final matchday of the 2011/12 Premier League season level on point with rivals United, but with a sizable advantage in goals difference. When the full time whistle was blown to signal the end of United's 1-0 win at Sunderland, City were trailing 2-1 as goals from QPR's Djibril Cisse and Jamie Mackie had canceled out Pablo Zabaleta's opener for City. Manchester City dug deep and found an equalizer through Edin Dzeko two minutes into added time. Two minutes later and at just the right moment, Balotelli nudged the ball towards Sergio Aguero who took a touch past the sprawling Taye Taiwo to set himself up before rifling into the QPR net. Martin Tyler, on commentary duty screamed "Aguerooooooooo" as the Argentine ripped off his shirt to mark the most iconic moment in Premier League history. Absolute delirium.

2. Former City captain and legendary defender, Vincent Kompany, labeled City's 1-0 win over rivals United in the 2010/11 FA Cup semifinal as a 'turning point," and he was right as that victory heralded the trophy-laden spell that soon followed. Ivorian midfielder Yaya Toure, a dominant midfielder for City in the early to mid-2010s intercepted United midfielder Michael Carrick's under hit pass to fire past Edwin van der Sar and send the blue half of Wembley into rapture.

3. Manchester City headed to London and the iconic Wembley Stadium to face Stoke City in the final of the 2010/11 FA Cup having not won a major honour for 35 years. Stoke City's goalkeeper Thomas Sorensen helped his side stay level with City for 74 minutes, before Yaya Toure smashed home the winner as he did in the semifinal victory over United a few weeks before.

4. Manchester City made the short trip across Manchester to face rivals United in October 2011 having won just once at Old Trafford in the league since 1974. A pair of braces from Mario Balotelli and Edin Dzeko and further goals from David Silva and Sergio Aguero helped City to an emphatic 6-1 win at their rivals' backyard, a statement victory that signaled the eventual changing of the guard from red to blue as the decade went on.

5. Manchester City welcomed rivals United to the Etihad Stadium three points behind the Red Devils but with a better goal difference three games to the end of the 2011/12 Premier League season. An evenly poised game played out, in contrast to the goal-fest at Old Trafford a few months back. City got the all-important winner through their captain and leader Vincent Kompany, who guided a header from a corner past United keeper David de Gea to set City up for one of the most thrilling finishes to an English top-flight season.

6. Manchester City travelled to Southampton's St Mary's Stadium on the final matchday of the 2017/18 Premier League season having already been confirmed as champions. A barren draw looked almost certain before City forward Gabriel Jesus raced away from the Southampton defence to slot home the goal that made City the first side to accumulate 100 points in a single season in English top-flight history.

7. Manchester City welcomed Liverpool to the Etihad Stadium in early January 2019 seven points adrift of the visitors midway through the 2018/19 Premier League season. City needed the win to close the gap and give themselves a better chance of retaining the title they had won in the previous season. City legend Sergio Aguero opened the scoring with a neat finish from close range but Liverpool equalized after the interval through Bobby Firmino, and pushed for a winner that left pocket of spaces in their backline for Raheem Sterling to expertly set Leroy Sane up for City's winner with less than 20 minutes left on the clock. That was Liverpool's only defeat that season as City beat them to the title by a single point.

8. Manchester City welcomed Brendan Rodgers' Leicester City in early May 2019 knowing any dropped points will see them cede the number position to Liverpool who had won earlier, heading into the final matchday of the 2018/19 Premier League season. The game remained deadlocked until the 70th minute when City's ever-reliable and talisman captain Vincent Kompany, playing in his

final game in front of the fans that had loved and adored him for over a decade, unleashed a rasping drive past Leicester keeper Kasper Schmeichel to settle the game and maintain City's advantage going into the final matchday.

9. Manchester City headed to England's Northeast in May 1968 in dire need of a win against Newcastle United at St James' Park to clinch only their second ever top-flight title and the first in 31 years. Mike Summerbee put the visitors ahead in the 14th minute but Newcastle responded immediately through Bryan Robson. City regained the lead thanks to Neil Young but Newcastle pulled level again before the interval through Jackie Sinclair. Neil added a second for City less than five minutes into the second half and City forward, Francis Lee, scored a fourth to give City a bit of breathing space. McNamee pulled a goal back for Newcastle with four minutes of normal time left, but City held on to become champions of England for a second time.

10. Manchester City recorded a 4-1 win over Tottenham Hotspur at Maine Road in December 1967 in a game dubbed as "Match of the Season" by BBC's Match of the Day highlights program. The game was played on a very cold and snowy winter day and City players, on the advice of the captain Tony Book were instructed to remove the outermost layer of leather from their studs so as to gain better grip on the expectedly slippery surface. Spurs legendary striker Jimmy Greaves gave his side an early lead, but Colin Bell soon equalized for City before the interval. Second half goals from former City forwards Mike Summerbee, Tony Coleman , and Neil Young wrapped up the win for City, who remained third after the win and went on to beat Manchester United to the title on the final day of that season.

BIGGEST TRANSFERS

"When you spend a lot of money on one player, you want him to prove himself, but the way football works, you can be good, the next you can be bad. I have come to Manchester City to work very hard and to help my friends make Manchester City great."

– Yaya Toure

20 Trivia Questions

1. Which of these clubs sold Pablo Zabaleta to Manchester City?

    A. West Ham

    B. Espanyol

    C. Sevilla

    D. Juventus

2. The second most expensive signing in the history of Manchester City is
_____?

    A. Jack Grealish

    B. Erling Haaland

    C. Kevin de Bruyne

    D. Ruben Dias

3. Portuguese center back , Ruben Dias, joined City from one of these clubs.

    A. Porto

    B. Braga

    C. Sporting Lisbon

    D. Benfica

4. Algerian forward, Riyad Mahrez, joined Manchester City in the summer of
_____?

    A. 2018

    B. 2017

    C. 2019

    D. 2016

5. Which of these City players joined the club in a player plus cash swap deal?

    A. Manuel Akanji

    B. Ruben Dias

    C. Joao Cancelo

    D. Robinho

6. City center back, Aymeric Laporte, joined the club in the January winter transfer window. What year did he join the club?

    A. 2017

    B. 2018

    C. 2019

    D. 2016

7. Which of these City defenders joined the club before the departure of Vincent Kompany?

    A. Nathan Ake

    B. Ruben Dias

    C. Aymeric Laporte

    D. Manuel Akanji

8. When did Nicolas Otamendi join Manchester City?

    A. 2010

    B. 2014

    C. 2017

    D. 2015

9. How old was Raheem Sterling when he was transferred to Manchester City?

   A. 20

   B. 23

   C. 19

   D. 22

10. Former England number one goalkeeper, Joe Hart, moved to City from one of these clubs.

    A. Macclesfield Town

    B. Shrewsbury Town

    C. Tranmere

    D. Blackpool

11. Where was Manchester City legend, Colin Bell, signed from?

    A. Bury

    B. Birmingham City

    C. Ipswich Town

    D. Millwall

12. Which of these former City players joined the club in 1998 from Bristol City?

    A. Bacary Sagna

    B. Ali Bernabia

    C. Shaun Goater

    D. Shaun Wright-Phillips

13. Which of these City players joined the club on a free transfer?

    A. Manuel Akanji

    B. Roque Santa Cruz

    C. Wilfried Bony

    D. Ali Bernabia

14. Where was former City captain, Andy Morrison, signed from?

    A. Huddersfield

    B. Plymouth

    C. Rotherham

    D. Oxford United

15. Where was former City forward, Lee Francis, joining the club from?

    A. Birmingham City

    B. Bolton Wanderers

    C. West Bromwich Albion

    D. Sunderland

16. Manchester City's record signing Jack Grealish was born in _____?

    A. Manchester

    B. London

    C. Birmingham

    D. Dublin

17. England defender John Stones arrived at Manchester City in the year _____?

    A. 2014

    B. 2017

    C. 2015

    D. 2016

18. Manchester City signed Argentina forward Julian Alvarez from one of these clubs.

    A. River Plate

    B. Boca Juniors

    C. Velez Sarsfield

    D. Independiente

19. Which of these former City players did not leave the club on a free transfer?

    A. James Milner

    B. Yaya Toure

    C. Jack Rodwell

    D. Fernandinho

20. Which of these players did not join City as a free agent?

    A. Stefan Ortega

    B. Willy Caballero

    C. Scott Carson

    D. Ali Bernabia

20 Trivia Answers

1. B – Espanyol

2. C – Kevin de Bruyne

3. D – Benfica

4. A – 2018

5. C – Joao Cancelo

6. B – 2018

7. C – Aymeric Laporte

8. D – 2015

9. A – 20

10. B – Shrewsbury Town

11. A – Bury

12. C – Shaun Goater

13. D – Ali Bernabia

14. A – Huddersfield

15. B – Bolton Wanderers

16. C – Birmingham

17. D – 2016

18. A – River Plate

19. C – Jack Rodwell

20. B – Willy Caballero

10 Fun Facts

1. Argentine forward, Sergio Aguero, joined Manchester City for a then club record fee of £35 million from Atletico Madrid in the summer of 2011. He instantly became a fan favourite, scoring a brace off the bench in his Premier League debut against Swansea City. He helped City to a first English top flight title in 44 years in his first season at the club, memorably scoring the winner in a 3-2 win over QPR on the final Premier League matchday of the 2011/12 season. He played 390 games for City and left in 2021 as the club's all-time highest goalscorer with 260 goals.

2. Belgium midfielder, Kevin de Bruyne, had just been named 2014/15 Bundesliga Player of the Year after helping VfL Wolfsburg to the German Cup when Manchester City made him their club record signing. He quickly dispelled any doubts that lingered from his underwhelming stay with Chelsea a few years before that with dazzling performances that has helped his club to ten major honours in his seven seasons at the club. He has also been named PFA and Premier League Player of the Season on two occasions each.

3. Manchester City signed Argentine forward, Carlos Tevez, in the summer of 2009 for £47 million from Media Sport Investment as the agency could not agree a deal with rivals United, whom he had spent the previous two seasons with and had helped win two Premier League titles and a Champions League title. He was entrusted with the City armband in his first season, and the gesture was kindly reciprocated as he helped end City's 35-year wait for a major honour by leading the club to the 2010/11 FA Cup. He helped add two Premier League titles and a League Cup in the following three seasons before he left for Juventus at the end of the 2013/14 season.

4. Manchester City parted with £26 million to acquire the services of Ivorian midfielder Yaya Toure from Barcelona in 2010. He instantly became a crucial part of City's team and played a significant role in ending the club's long wait for a major honour with winning goals in the semifinal and final of the 2010/11 FA Cup.

5. Belgian centre back , Vincent Kompany, is one of the Premier League's best ever bargain purchases, not just City's. The £7 million City paid to sign him from Hamburg in 2008 seems utterly ridiculous when one pores through his immense contributions to the success the club achieved during his time there. He scored twenty goals across his 360 City appearances and won twelve trophies, eleven as club captain.

6. Brazilian midfielder, Fernandinho, made over 300 City appearances spanning across his nine-year association with the club that began in the summer of 2013 when he joined for £34 million from Shakhtar Donetsk. He shored up City's midfield allowing the likes of David Silva, Yaya Toure, and Kevin de Bruyne to express their offensive capabilities. He became City captain in his final two seasons and led the club to successive Premier League titles.

7. Argentine defender, Pablo Zabaleta, was signed for a paltry £7 million pounds a day before the Abu Dhabi United Group's takeover of the club was completed. He proved an absolute steal, establishing himself as one of the best right-backs in European football. He won six major honours before he left the club in 2017.

8. The £55 million pounds City shelled out in 2015 to sign young Liverpool winger, Raheem Sterling, seemed like a gamble at the time as the England forward showed as much inconsistency as talent back then. His first season at City yielded just six goals and two assists, but he experienced a positive turn around when Pep Guardiola arrived at the club, scoring 35 goals across two seasons as City won back-to-back Premier League titles in 2017/18 and 2018/19. Sterling helped add two further Premier League titles, five League Cups, one community (charity) shield, and one FA Cup before he was transferred to Chelsea in 2022.

9. Manchester City paid Benfica £35 million pounds for the services of Brazilian goalkeeper, Ederson, following Claudio Bravo's struggles to adapt to the English game in the previous season. Ederson settled in quickly, combining smart saves with impeccable ball-playing ability from deep that rapidly turned defense into attacks as City coasted to the Premier League with a record 100 points in his first season at the club.

10. Spanish European Championship and World Cup winner, David Silva, was signed from La Liga side Valencia CF for £26 million pounds in the summer of 2010. He made over 400 appearances for City and scored 77 goals in addition to the 147 assists and eleven major honours he helped the club win in a highly successful 10-year stay.

RECORD BREAKERS

"The fact that an Englishman has an Argentinian as an idol is very rare. I keep watching my (title-winning) goal against QPR and every time I get more emotional. My plan is to stay here because I'm convinced Manchester City will be at the same level as Real Madrid and Barcelona."

– Sergio Aguero

20 Trivia Questions

1. When did Manchester City set a new Premier League record for most successive wins?

    A. 2011/12

    B. 2019/20

    C. 2017/18

    D. 2016/17

2. Which other side has matched City's Premier League record for most successive wins?

    A. Manchester United

    B. Chelsea

    C. Arsenal

    D. Liverpool

3. Which of these former players holds the record for most goals scored by a City player in one season?

    A. Tommy Johnson

    B. Neil Young

    C. Francis Lee

    D. Sergio Aguero

4. Manchester City set an English top-flight record of 21 wins in a row in all competitions in which of these seasons?

   A. 2019/20

   B. 2020/21

   C. 2017/18

   D. 2018/19

5. How many consecutive home league wins were recorded by City between March 2011 and March 2012?

   A. 14

   B. 18

   C. 20

   D. 21

6. How many games does City's club record unbeaten run consist of?

   A. 22

   B. 28

   C. 32

   D. 24

7. How many games were there in City's Premier League record for longest winning streak in a calendar year?

   A. 12

   B. 14

   C. 10

   D. 13

8. City set an English record for the highest number of wins in one month in _____?

    A. January 2021

    B. March 2021

    C. April 2021

    D. February 2021

9. What is the highest number of Manchester City clean sheets in all competitions in a single season?

    A. 26

    B. 33

    C. 30

    D. 35

10. Which City keeper has kept the most clean sheets for the club in a single season?

    A. Bert Trautmann

    B. Ederson

    C. Joe Hart

    D. Claudio Bravo

11. Manchester City's biggest victory in the English Football League was recorded against _____?

    A. Lincoln City

    B. Plymouth Argyle

    C. Swindon Town

    D. Oxford United

12. Who were the opponents for City's biggest FA Cup win?

    A. Everton

    B. Arsenal

    C. Leeds United

    D. Liverpool

13. Which of these former City players won the most international caps?

    A. Sergio Aguero

    B. Vincent Kompany

    C. David Silva

    D. Yaya Toure

14. City's biggest ever win in European club competition was recorded against _____?

    A. Copenhagen

    B. Schalke 04

    C. Villareal

    D. CSKA Moscow

15. City's biggest ever win in the FA Cup final was recorded against _____?

    A. Watford

    B. Portsmouth

    C. Leicester City

    D. Birmingham City

16. What is the highest number of consecutive clean sheets kept by City in the league?

    A. 9

    B. 8

    C. 7

    D. 6

17. How many games did City's longest unbeaten run in the Champions League last for?

    A. 10

    B. 11

    C. 12

    D. 13

18. How many games did City's longest unbeaten home run in the Champions League last for?

    A. 14

    B. 12

    C. 13

    D. 11

19. City hold the record for the longest winning streak by an English team in the Champions League. How many games did the run span?

    A. 6

    B. 7

    C. 8

    D. 9

20. How many consecutive away games have City won in all competitions in the club's entire history?

    A. 12

    B. 15

    C. 17

    D. 19

20 Trivia Answers

1. C – 2017/18

2. D – Liverpool

3. A – Tommy Johnson

4. B – 2020/21

5. C – 20

6. B – 28

7. D – 13

8. A – January 2021

9. B – 33

10. C – Joe Hart

11. A – Lincoln City

12. D – Liverpool

13. C – David Silva

14. B – Schalke 04

15. A – Watford

16. D – 6

17. C – 12

18. A – 14

19. B – 7

20. D – 19

10 Fun Facts

1. English midfielder, Alan Oakes, is City's club record appearance holder. He signed his first professional contract at the club in 1959 after joining a year prior as an amateur, and went on to feature 680 times, scoring 34 goals. He won seven major honours with Manchester City before he moved on to Chester City in July 1976.

2. Argentine forward, Sergio Aguero, is the most prolific player in the history of Manchester City. He joined the club in the summer of 2011 and won the club its first championship in 44 years with the last kick of the 2011/12 Premier League season. He helped the club add a further 11 major honours and scored a total of 260 goals in 390 appearances across all competitions before he joined Barcelona as a free agent in the summer of 2021.

3. Manchester City are the first English club to win a domestic treble. The club pipped Liverpool to the 2018/19 Premier League by a single point and enjoyed success in the League Cup and FA Cup, beating Chelsea and Watford respectively.

4. Manchester City are the only team in Premier League history to amass 100 points in a single season. The club achieved the feat in the 2017/18 season when they won 32 out of their 38 league games and dropped only 14 points out of a possible 114 across a 38-game league season.

5. Manchester City scored 106 Premier League goals in their 2017/18 title-winning campaign. The club record for most league goals in a season is 108, set in 1926/27 (Division Two, 42 games) and 2001/02 (Division One, 46 games).

6. In the 2018/19 season, Manchester City scored a total of 169 goals to set a new English record for most goals scored across all competitions in a single season.

7. Manchester City scored a total of 113 Premier League goals in 2021 to set a new record for most goals scored by a Premier League team in one calendar year. In the same year, the club also set a record for number of Premier League wins in a calendar year with 36 victories and a record for most away league wins with 19 victories.

8. Manchester City have won a record 32 Premier League games in a single season on two occasions. The record is shared with Liverpool, who also won 32 league games in the 2019/20 season.

9. In March 1934, a record 84,569 spectators attended City's FA Cup tie against Stoke City at Manchester City's former Maine Road Stadium. That number represents the highest ever recorded at any ground in England (excluding Wembley National Stadium).

10. Brazilian midfielder, Fernandinho, has played more games for City in European club competition than any other player in the club's history. All of his 75 appearances in European club competitions for City were made in the UEFA Champions League between 2013 and 2022.

FINAL WHISTLE

Hello there, our fellow *footBaller*.

We really hope you enjoyed The Best Manchester City Trivia Book Ever. And, congratulations on reading it to the end!

We create these books to allow football fans to expand their knowledge around their favourite clubs and players, but most importantly, to keep the passion we all have for the game lit and alive.

Life can come with many challenges and setbacks. But something that never leaves our side is our love for the game.

If you enjoyed reading this book, we'd like to kindly ask for your feedback and thoughts in the review section on Amazon. This would really encourage us to keep creating the highest quality books and content for football fans across the globe.

This QR code takes you directly to leave a rating on Amazon. :)

Thanks in advance!

Ball out,

The House of Ballers team.

Made in United States
North Haven, CT
26 November 2023

44594726R00075